LAUBACH WAY TO ENGLISH

W9-BMA-534

WORKBOOK FOR

SKILL BOOK *1*

LAUBACH WAY TO READING

Jeanette D. Macero

ISBN 0-88336-371-2

© 1985, 1991

New Readers Press

Division of ProLiteracy Worldwide
1320 Jamesville Ave., Syracuse, New York 13210

Printed in the United States of America

Edited by Kay Koschnick

Designed by Chris Steenwerth

Illustrated by Cheri Bladholm

20   19   18   17

To the Teacher

This *Workbook for Skill Book 1* is designed to give students additional practice in listening to, speaking, reading, and writing the patterns of English presented in *Skill Book 1*. The vocabulary is controlled to the reading vocabulary taught at each lesson level in *Skill Book 1*, although some new words are introduced.

The workbook gives practice in 14 skill areas, all of which are important in mastering English. (See the chart titled "Workbook at a Glance" on the next page.)

There are exercises on the chart words, singular and plural forms of nouns, and on the use of pronouns, articles, and prepositions. Students learn verb forms in the simple present and present progressive tenses. They make and answer questions in the affirmative and negative.

One type of exercise in the workbook is a much modified cloze exercise, here titled "Write the Missing Words." These exercises, taken from *Skill Book 1* stories, are sentences in which a word is left blank. Any grammatically correct and logical word is acceptable as an answer.

Listening exercises are included to sharpen the students' ability to hear the difference between singular and plural verb forms and between verb endings—forms that are often difficult for students to differentiate. Students are also asked to listen and then write what they hear.

An answer key is not provided since it is not recommended that students at this level check their own work. *You* should check their work so that you can help them understand and correct their errors. Also, your judgment is needed in cases where more than one answer is possible. Be sure to praise students for completing the exercise and for their correct answers. If a student gives correct answers that go beyond what has been taught, praise him for his knowledge of the language.

How to Use the Exercises

The exercises for each lesson are arranged in increasing order of difficulty. Some exercise pages have a note at the bottom that gives specific instructions to the teacher. In general, however, the following steps are useful for the majority of exercises.

1. Teach any new words listed in notes to the teacher at the bottom of the page. (Point to their first occurrence in the exercise instructions or exercise.)

2. Read the directions aloud to the students. Never assign an exercise without being sure that the students know what is required in it.

3. Go over the example that is given for each exercise. (The answer is supplied.) Have the students do one exercise

item. Then check their work. Praise them if it is correct. If a student's answer is incorrect, explain the error. Have the student write the correct answer and read the item aloud. If a student still cannot do the exercise, go over the example again and do one or two exercise items with him.

4. Have the students follow the directions carefully and keep the sentences in the tenses given.

Tips on Specific Types of Exercises

Most exercises for a particular lesson can be assigned as homework, along with the homework for that lesson in *Skill Book 1*.

Verb forms. Point out the words (for example, *girl* or *girls*) that indicate the form of the verb to be used.

Writing missing words. Go over the words the students write. Check for errors, and explain in simple terms anything that is wrong. Praise students for whatever they can write correctly. If the students cannot write words on their own, do some sample exercises orally. Have the students write these words. Then reassign the exercises for homework, asking the students to write different items.

Listening exercises. Unlike other exercises, these must be done in class. In some of these exercises, the students hear a sentence and are asked to identify the picture it refers to. (For variety, the teacher can point to a picture, and have the student say a sentence identifying it.) Do one or two examples with the students, repeating them if necessary. Read the sentences in a natural manner at a regular pace. Do not emphasize the items being taught or enunciate the words with extra care. If students have difficulty with a listening exercise, do it again at another time.

In the "Listen and Write" exercise, the students listen to the teacher and fill in the missing word. For example, the teacher reads "This is Mr. Oliver." The student sees *This _____ Mr. Oliver* and writes *is* in the blank.

How to Vary the Exercises

While most of the exercises were designed primarily to be used as homework, they may also be used to advantage in class or while tutoring.

1. Some of the exercises may be done orally with books closed. Help students with their pronunciation and intonation at this time.

2. Have the students do the exercises as homework. Then at the next class session, have them read the answers to you. Listen for pronunciation and intonation errors. Have students imitate your pronunciation of words.

phrases, and sentences that cause difficulty. In a class situation, students can work in pairs with one student identifying a picture or asking the questions and the other giving the answers.

3. In later lessons, some exercises can be used for dictation, for example the "Listen and Say," "Listen and Write," and any exercise on verb forms. First, read the entire sentence at a normal pace; do not enunciate in an exaggerated manner. Next, dictate the sentence in meaningful segments, reading each segment twice.

When dictation is still difficult for students, the sentence *This / is / Mr. Oliver* can be read in the segments marked by the slashes. As students become more proficient with dictation exercises, the segments can be longer and can be read once instead of twice, for example: *This is / Mr. Oliver.*

Give the students time to look over what they have written. Read the sentence again at a normal pace so students can check any parts they have doubts about.

Finally, have the students correct their sentences according to the model in the workbook. If they make their corrections in a different color, you can easily see what mistakes they are making. It is important for you to look over the dictation. The errors will give you invaluable insight into the students' learning processes and show you where the students need more practice.

The Workbook at a Glance

Skill areas	Lesson and practice numbers
Chart words	1-1, 2-1, 3-1, 5-1, 10-2
Nouns	2-2, 3-3, 6-4, 8-1, 8-2, 9-1, 12-1, 13-2
Pronouns	4-2, 5-3, 6-1, 11-4, 13-5
Verbs	7-1, 7-3, 9-4, 10-1, 12-3
Numbers	11-2, 11-9, 12-2
Prepositions	3-2, 4-3, 5-2, 6-3, 7-2, 8-3, 9-2, 9-3, 11-1, 13-3, 13-4
Articles	4-4, 6-2
Make Questions	11-5, 12-4, 12-7, 13-1
Answer Questions	11-7, 11-8, 12-5, 12-6, 12-8, 12-9
Make negative sentences	11-3, 11-6
Listen and say	1-3, 2-3, 3-4, 4-5, 5-4
Listen and write	7-4, 8-4, 9-5, 10-4, 11-10, 12-10, 13-6
Write missing words	1-2, 4-1, 10-3
Practice writing	A, B, C, D-F

PRACTICE for UNIT A: Student's Name

Note to the teacher: Using pp. 24-25 of the *ESOL Teacher's Manual for Skill Book 1* as a guide, print the student's name on the first line as a model for him to copy.

PRACTICE for UNIT B: Copy Numbers

1 1

2 2,

3 3

4 4

5 5

6 6

7 7

8 8

9 9

10 10

PRACTICE for UNIT C: Name, Address, Telephone Number

Name:

_____

Address:

_____

Telephone:

_____

Name:

_____

Address:

_____

Telephone:

_____

PRACTICE for UNITS D-F: Copy Numbers

11	5
12	10
13	15
14	20
15	25
16	30
17	35
18	40
19	45
20	50

Note to the teacher: The first column may be used after Unit D and the second column after Unit F.

PRACTICE 1: Chart Words

bird	dish	girl
cup	fish	hand

1. The girl has a __bird__ .

2. The girl has a _____ .

3. The girl has a _____ .

4. The girl has a _____ .

5. The girl has a _____ .

6. The _____ has a bird.

PRACTICE 2: Write the Missing Words

1. The girl has a bird in her hand.

2. The __girl__ has a bird in her hand.

3. The girl has _____ bird in her hand.

4. The girl _____ a bird in her hand.

5. The girl has a _____ in her hand.

6. The girl has a bird _____ her hand.

7. The girl has a bird in _____ hand.

8. The girl has a bird in her _____ .

PRACTICE 3: Listen and Say

---

1. Teacher says the sentence. The student identifies the corresponding picture.

   Teacher: This is a bird.
   Student: [Points to picture of bird.]

   Teacher: This is a cup.
   This is a hand.
   This is a fish.
   This is a girl.
   This is a dish.
   This is a bird.

2. Reverse the procedure.
   Teacher points to picture; student says sentence.
   Help the student with pronunciation if necessary.

PRACTICE 1: Chart Words

jumping	leg	neck
kicking	man	pan

1. This is a _____ .

2. This is a _____ .

3. This is a _____ .

4. This is a _____ .

5. The girl is _____ .

6. The man is _____ .

PRACTICE 2: Write *man's* **or** *girl's*

1. The man has a pan.   This is the __man's__ pan.

2. The girl has a cup.   This is the _____ cup.

3. The man has a neck.   This is the _____ neck.

4. The girl has a leg.   This is the _____ leg.

5. The man has a fish.   This is the _____ fish.

6. The girl has a dish.   This is the _____ dish.

7. The man has a pan.   This is the _____ pan.

PRACTICE 3: Listen and Say

1. Teacher says the sentence. The student identifies the corresponding picture.

   Teacher: This is a man.
   Student: [Points to picture of a man.]

   Teacher: This is a leg.
   This is a neck.
   This is a pan.
   This is a man.
   The man is kicking.
   The girl is jumping.

2. Reverse the procedure.
   Teacher points to picture; student says sentence.
   Help the student with pronunciation if necessary.

PRACTICE 1: Chart Words

river	tent	woman
snake	valley	yells

1. This is a _____ .

2. This is a _____ .

3. This is a _____ .

4. This is a _____ .

5. This is a _____ .

6. The man _____ .

PRACTICE 2: Write *in, at*

1. The river is ___in___ the valley.

2. The tent is _____ the river.

3. The man is _____ the tent.

4. The woman is _____ the tent.

5. The woman is _____ the river.

6. The river is _____ the valley.

PRACTICE 3: Write *man's, girl's, woman's*

1. The girl has a pan.

   This is the ___girl's___ pan.

2. The woman has a tent.

   This is the _____ tent.

3. The man has a snake.

   This is the _____ snake.

4. The woman has a cup.

   This is the _____ cup.

5. The girl has a bird.

   This is the _____ bird.

6. The man has a dish.

   This is the _____ dish.

7. The girl has a dish.

   This is the _____ dish.

8. The woman has a bird.

   This is the _____ bird.

PRACTICE 4: Listen and Say

---

1. Teacher says the sentence. The student identifies the corresponding picture.

   Teacher: This is a river.
   Student: [Points to picture of a river.]

   Teacher: This is a valley.
   This is a snake.
   This is a river.
   This is a woman.
   This is a tent.
   The man yells, "Look!"

2. Reverse the procedure.
   Teacher points to picture; student says sentence.
   Help the student with pronunciation if necessary.

PRACTICE 1: Write the Missing Words

1. This is an apple.

   This __is__ an apple.

   This is _____ apple.

   This is an _____ .

2. The man gives the apple to the woman.

   The man gives _____ apple to the woman.

   _____ man gives the apple to the woman.

   The man _____ the apple to the woman.

   The man gives the _____ to the woman.

3. The woman puts the apple in her dish.

   The _____ puts the apple in her dish.

   The woman puts _____ apple in her dish.

   The woman _____ the apple _____ her dish.

   The woman _____ the _____ in her _____ .

PRACTICE 2: Write *He* or *She*

1. The man picks up the apple.

   __He__ picks up the apple.

2. The woman has the apple.

   _____ has the apple.

3. The man has the apple in his hand.

   _____ has the apple in his hand.

4. The woman puts the apple in her dish.

   _____ puts the apple in her dish.

5. The girl is jumping.

   _____ is jumping.

6. The man gives the apple to the woman.

   _____ gives the apple to the woman.

7. The girl picks up the apple.

   _____ picks up the apple.

8. The woman gives the apple to the girl.

   _____ gives the apple to the girl.

PRACTICE 3: Write *in* **or** *at*

1. The man is ___in___ the tent.

2. The man is _____ the river.

3. The snake is _____ the tent.

4. The man has the apple _____ his hand.

5. She puts the egg _____ her dish.

6. The woman has the apple _____ her hand.

PRACTICE 4: Write *a* **or** *an*

1. The girl has ___a___ bird.

2. The man has _____ dish.

3. She has _____ egg.

4. The woman gives _____ apple to the man.

5. The man has _____ cup.

6. She puts _____ olive in her dish.

7. The girl has _____ pan.

8. She gives _____ apple to the woman.

PRACTICE 5: Listen and Say

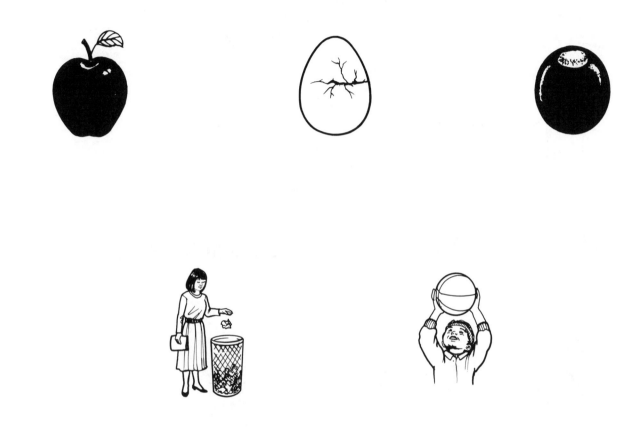

1. Teacher says the sentence. The student identifies the corresponding picture.

   Teacher: This is an egg.
   Student: [Points to picture of an egg.]

   Teacher: This is an olive.
   This is an apple.
   This is an egg.
   The man put *up* his hands.
   The woman puts the apple *in* the can.

2. Reverse the procedure.
   Teacher points to picture; student says sentence.
   Help the student with pronunciation if necessary.

PRACTICE 1: Chart Words

box   quarter   children

zipper   shop   thank

1. This is a _____ .

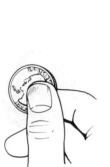

2. The _____ is in the shop.

3. This is a _____ .

4. This is a _____ .

5. The _____ get a dish.

6. They _____ him for the dish.

PRACTICE 2: Write *to* or **or** *for*

1. The man gives the apple __to__ the woman.

2. He sells the box _____ a quarter.

3. The children thank him _____ the zipper.

4. He gives the egg _____ the woman.

5. They thank him _____ the pan.

6. He sells the dish _____ a quarter.

7. They thank him _____ the box.

8. He gives the box _____ the woman.

PRACTICE 3: Write *He, She* **or** *They*

1. The children get a box.

   __They__ get a box.

2. The man sells the box.

   _____ sells the box.

3. The girl has the apple.

   _____ has the apple.

4. The woman puts the apple in her dish.

   _____ puts the apple in her dish.

5. The man picks up the apple.

   _____ picks up the apple.

6. The children thank him for the pan.

   _____ thank him for the pan.

7. The man sells the box for a quarter.

   _____ sells the box for a quarter.

8. The children thank him for the zipper.

   _____ thank him for the zipper.

PRACTICE 4: Listen and Say

1. Teacher says the sentence. The student identifies the corresponding picture.

   Teacher: This is a zipper.
   Student: [Points to picture of a zipper.]

   Teacher: This is a box.
              This is a quarter.
              This is a zipper.
              This is a shop.
              They are children.
              He says thank you.

2. Reverse the procedure.
   Teacher points to picture; student says sentence.
   Help the student with pronunciation if necessary.

PRACTICE 1: Write *He, She* **or** *They*

1. Ann is a woman.

   __She__ is a woman.

2. Bob is a boy.

   _____ is a boy.

3. Cal gives a bird to Bob.

   _____ gives a bird to Bob.

4. The children give a fish to Fran.

   _____ give a fish to Fran.

5. Ann and Fran give a dish to Dan.

   _____ give a dish to Dan.

6. Bob and Cal give a bird to Ed.

   _____ give a bird to Ed.

7. Fran is a girl.

   _____ is a girl.

8. Dan and Ed give a fish to Fran.

   _____ give a fish to Fran.

PRACTICE 2: Write *a* **or** *an*

1. Ann is ___a___ woman.

2. She gives _____ cup to Cal.

3. She gives _____ egg to Bob.

4. Fran is _____ girl.

5. Fran gives _____ apple to Ann.

6. Bob is _____ boy.

7. Bob gives _____ olive to Fran.

8. Dan gives _____ quarter to Ed.

PRACTICE 3: Write *to* **or** *for*

1. The man gives the apple __to__ the woman.

2. He sells the box _____ a quarter.

3. The children thank him _____ the zipper.

4. He gives an egg _____ Ed.

5. They thank him _____ the pan.

6. He sells the dish _____ a quarter.

7. Ann gives a bird _____ Bob.

8. She thanks him _____ the fish.

PRACTICE 4: Write the Word with -'s

Ann's   Cal's   Ed's

Bob's   Dan's   Fran's

1. Ann has an apple.   This is <u>Ann's</u> apple.

2. Fran has a fish.   This is _____ fish.

3. Bob has a bird.   This is _____ bird.

4. Ed has an egg.   This is _____ egg.

5. Dan has a dish.   This is _____ dish.

6. Cal has a cup.   This is _____ cup.

7. Ann has an apple.   This is _____ apple.

PRACTICE 1: Write *is* or **are**

1. This ___is___ Jill Hill.

2. This _____ Indian Valley.

3. Glenn _____ fishing in the river.

4. Glenn and Liz _____ fishing in the river.

5. Jill _____ jumping.

6. Jill and Kim _____ at the river.

7. Liz Hill _____ looking at her girls.

8. The children _____ at the river.

PRACTICE 2: Write *in* or *at*

1. Glenn Hill lives ___in___ Indian Valley.

2. Jill and Kim are _____ the river.

3. Glenn is fishing _____ the river.

4. Kim lives _____ Indian Valley.

5. The egg is _____ the dish.

6. The box is _____ the shop.

7. The river is _____ the valley.

8. The woman is _____ the river.

PRACTICE 3: Words with -ing

Add -ing. Write the word. Write the sentence.

1. Jill is jumping.   *jumping*

   Jill is jumping.

2. Kim is jump___. _____

   _____

3. Glenn is look___ at his girls. _____

   _____

4. Liz is look___ at her girls. _____

   _____

5. Glenn is fish___ in the river. _____

   _____

6. Liz is fish___ in the river. _____

   _____

7. Jack is kick___. _____

   _____

8. Kim is jump___. _____

   _____

PRACTICE 4: Listen and Write

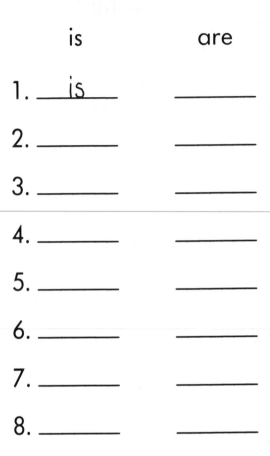

	is	are
1.	is	_____
2.	_____	_____
3.	_____	_____
4.	_____	_____
5.	_____	_____
6.	_____	_____
7.	_____	_____
8.	_____	_____

Teacher says: Listen to the sentence.
If you hear *is* in the sentence, write *is*.
If you hear *are*, write *are*.

Teacher reads: 1. This is Jill Hill.
2. Glenn and Liz are at the river.
3. Kim is jumping.
4. Glenn is fishing in the river.
5. Glenn and Liz are fishing in the river.
6. The children are at the river.
7. Liz is looking at her girls.
8. The girls are jumping.

PRACTICE 1: Write the Word with -s

1 bird   2 __birds__

1 pup   2 _____

1 snake   2 _____

1 pet   2 _____

1 cup   2 _____

1 boy   2 _____

1 egg   2 _____

1 apple   2 _____

1 girl   2 _____

1 olive   2 _____

PRACTICE 2: Write the Words

Mr. Oliver's   Mr. Hill's   pup's

Mrs. Oliver's   Mrs. Hill's

1. Mr. Oliver has a pup.

   Queen is <u>Mr. Oliver's</u> pup.

2. The pup has a dish.

   This is the _____ dish.

3. Mr. Hill has a box.

   This is _____ box.

4. Mrs. Oliver has a dish.

   This is _____ dish.

5. Mr. Hill has a quarter.

   This is _____ quarter.

6. Mrs. Hill has a zipper.

   This is _____ zipper.

7. Mr. Oliver has a tent.

   This is _____ tent.

8. Mrs. Oliver has an egg.

   This is _____ egg.

9. Mrs. Hill has a pan.

   This is _____ pan.

10. The pup has a dish in the box.   The _____ dish is in the box.

PRACTICE 3: Write *to, up, at, in*

1. Queen runs __to__ Mr. Oliver.

2. Mr. Oliver picks _____ the pup.

3. Pam puts the pup's dish _____ the box.

4. Glenn Hill is looking _____ his girls.

5. Fran gives an apple _____ Ann.

6. Queen runs _____ Mrs. Oliver.

7. The man picks _____ the apple.

8. Liz Hill is looking _____ her girls.

PRACTICE 4: Listen and Write

Listen to the teacher. Write the missing word.

1. This __is__ Mr. Oliver.

   _____ is Queen.

   Queen _____ to Mr. Oliver.

   Queen runs to _____ Oliver.

   Mr. Oliver picks up _____ pup.

2. This is _____ Oliver.

   Queen _____ to Mrs. Oliver.

   Queen runs to _____ Oliver.

   Mrs. Oliver picks up _____ pup.

Teacher reads: 1. This is Mr. Oliver.
                 This is Queen.
                 Queen runs to Mr. Oliver.
                 Queen runs to Mr. Oliver.
                 Mr. Oliver picks up the pup.

2. This is Mrs. Oliver.
    Queen runs to Mrs. Oliver.
    Queen runs to Mrs. Oliver.
    Mrs. Oliver picks up the pup.

PRACTICE 1: Write the Word with -s

1 pet   2 ___pets___

1 bird   2 _____

1 snake   2 _____

1 pet shop   2 _____

1 street   2 _____

1 river   2 _____

1 tent   2 _____

1 valley   2 _____

1 pup   2 _____

1 leg   2 _____

PRACTICE 2: Write *in, on, at*

1. Uncle Ted lives __on__ York Street.

2. The pet shop is _____ York Street.

3. The boys are _____ the pet shop.

4. A snake is _____ the box.

5. An egg is _____ the dish.

6. Will is _____ the pet shop.

7. The woman is _____ the river.

8. The pup's dish is _____ the box.

9. Liz is fishing _____ the river.

10. He lives _____ Indian Valley.

PRACTICE 3:   **Write** *at, up, to, for*

1. Sam yells, "Look __at__ the snake."

2. Uncle Ted picks _____ the snake.

3. The boys are looking _____ the pups.

4. Ann gives a bird _____ Bob.

5. Fran says, "Thank you _____ the apple."

6. He sells the box _____ a quarter.

7. The man picks _____ the egg.

8. The children thank him _____ the box.

PRACTICE 4: Write *live* **or** *lives*

1. Uncle Ted __lives__ on York Street.

2. The boys _____ on York Street.

3. Glenn Hill _____ in Indian Valley.

4. Glenn and Liz _____ in Indian Valley.

5. Jill _____ in Indian Valley.

6. Jill and Kim _____ in Indian Valley.

7. Sam _____ on York Street.

8. The boys _____ on York Street.

PRACTICE 5: Listen and Write

Listen to the teacher. Write the missing word.

1. The boys are __at__ the pet shop.

2. Uncle Ted lives _____ York Street.

3. A snake is _____ the box.

4. The boys are looking _____ the fish.

5. Uncle Ted gives a pup _____ Pam.

6. Sam yells, "Look _____ the snake!"

7. Uncle Ted picks _____ the snake.

8. Sam is going _____ the pet shop.

9. Uncle Ted has a pet shop _____ York Street.

Note to the teacher: The words to be used in the blanks are the prepositions *at, in, on, to, up.*

PRACTICE 1: Write *is* or *are*

1. This man __is__ Mr. Hill.

2. Mr. and Mrs. Hill _____ at the river.

3. They _____ fishing in the river.

4. The girl _____ Jill Hill.

5. The Hills _____ at the tent.

6. This woman _____ Mrs. Hill.

7. Ed and Jill _____ fishing.

8. The fish _____ in a pan.

9. The boy _____ Ed Hill.

10. The Hills _____ looking at the fish.

PRACTICE 2: Write *The Hills* **or** *The Olivers*

1. Mr. and Mrs. Hill are at the river.

   <u>The Hills</u> are at the river.

2. Mr. and Mrs. Oliver pet the pup.

   _____ pet the pup.

3. Mr. and Mrs. Hill live in Indian Valley.

   _____ live in Indian Valley.

4. Mr. and Mrs. Oliver put the pup in a box.

   _____ put the pup in a box.

PRACTICE 3: Write the Missing Words

1. This man is <u>Mr.</u> Hill.

2. This woman is _____ Hill.

3. This man is _____ Hill.

4. _____ and _____ Oliver have a pup.

5. They are fishing _____ the river.

6. The fish are _____ a pan.

7. The fish are in _____ pan.

8. The fish are in a _____ .

PRACTICE 4: Listen and Write

Listen to the teacher. Write the missing word.

gets   gives   puts

1. Mr. Hill _____ a fish.

2. He _____ the fish in a dish.

3. He _____ the fish to the children.

4. Mrs. Hill _____ a fish.

5. Ed _____ the fish to the children.

6. Ed _____ the fish in a pan.

Note to the teacher: Read the appropriate verb in each sentence.

PRACTICE 1: Write *in, on, at*

1. Mr. and Mrs. Hill live __in__ Indian Valley.

2. The Olivers live _____ River Street.

3. They live _____ 426 River Street.

4. The pet shop is _____ York Street.

5. The pet shop is not _____ Indian Valley.

6. The pet shop is _____ 3574 York Street.

7. Mrs. Bird lives _____ 9 Valley Street.

8. Cal lives _____ Valley Street.

PRACTICE 2: Write the Numbers

_5_	_25_	___	___	___
_10_	___	___	___	___
_15_	___	___	___	___
_20_	___	___	___	___

PRACTICE 3: Make a Sentence with *not*

1. River Street is in Indian Valley.

   River Street is not in Indian Valley.

2. Mrs. Bird is going to York Street.

   _____

3. Uncle Ted's pet shop is in Indian Valley.

   _____

4. York Street is in Indian Valley.

   _____

5. Mr. and Mrs. Hill are at the pet shop.

   _____

6. They are looking at the pup.

   _____

7. The egg is in the dish.

   _____

8. The pup is in the box.

   _____

PRACTICE 4: **Write** *his, her, their*

1. Uncle Ted's pet shop is on York Street.

   __His__ pet shop is on York Street.

2. Uncle Ted's snake is in the box.

   _____ snake is in the box.

3. Mrs. Bird and Cal live in Indian Valley.

   She and _____ boy live in Indian Valley.

4. Mr. and Mrs. Hill live in Indian Valley.

   _____ telephone number is 234-9169.

5. Mr. and Mrs. Oliver live on River Street.

   _____ telephone number is 446-5541.

6. Mr. Oliver's pup is in the box.

   _____ pup is in the box.

7. Queen is Mr. Oliver's pup.

   Queen is _____ pup.

8. Jill's fish are in the pan.

   _____ fish are in the pan.

PRACTICE 5: Make Questions

1. Queen is Mr. Oliver's pup.

   <u>Is Queen Mr. Oliver's pup?</u>

2. Uncle Ted's shop is on York Street.

   _____

3. Mr. and Mrs. Hill are at the river.

   _____

4. They are fishing in the river.

   _____

5. Ed is fishing in the river.

   _____

6. The Hills are at the tent.

   _____

7. The snake is a pet.

   _____

8. Liz is looking at her girls.

   _____

Note to the teacher: Encourage the student to use question marks.

PRACTICE 6: Make a Sentence with *not*

1. Uncle Ted's pet shop is in Indian Valley.

   Uncle Ted's pet shop is not in Indian Valley.

2. His pet shop is at 2564 York Street.

   _____

3. Ed is going to York Street.

   _____

4. River Street is in Indian Valley.

   _____

5. York Street is in Indian Valley.

   _____

6. The fish are jumping in the river.

   _____

7. Ed and Jill are at the river.

   _____

8. Kim is jumping.

   _____

PRACTICE 7: Answer the Questions with *Yes*

1. Is Ed fishing?

   Yes, he is.

2. Is Mrs. Hill fishing?

   _____

3. Is Jill fishing?

   _____

4. Is Ed fishing?

   _____

5. Are the Hills at the tent?

   _____

6. Is Will at the pet shop?

   _____

7. Are the boys looking at the birds?

   _____

8. Are Glenn and Liz fishing?

   _____

Note to the teacher: The word *yes* is new here.

PRACTICE 8: Answer the Questions with *No*

1. Is Uncle Ted in Indian Valley?

   No, he isn't.

2. Is Mrs. Oliver on York Street?

   _____

3. Is Will at the river?

   _____

4. Is Mrs. Hill going to the pet shop?

   _____

5. Is Mrs. Oliver fishing?

   _____

6. Is Uncle Ted fishing?

   _____

7. Is Mr. Oliver in the pet shop?

   _____

8. Is Liz Hill jumping and kicking?

   _____

Note to the teacher: The words *no* and *isn't* are new here.

PRACTICE 9: Telephone Numbers

Fire _____

Home _____

Police _____

Work _____

PRACTICE 10: Listen and Write

Listen to the teacher. Write the numbers.

1. They live at ___19___ Valley Street.

2. She lives at _____ Valley Street.

3. They live at _____ River Street.

4. Mr. Oliver lives at _____ River Street.

5. The pet shop is at _____ York Street.

6. His telephone number is _____ .

Notes to the teacher: In Practice 9, supply the numbers for the fire and police
departments and help students write them, plus their numbers
for home and work.

In Practice 10, use different numbers in each sentence.
Numbers like 17 and 70 or 19 and 90, which are difficult for
students to differentiate, are useful to practice.

PRACTICE 1: Write the Word

One child   Two   ___children___

One boy   Three   _____

One bird   Four   _____

One girl   Five   _____

One child   Six   _____

PRACTICE 2: Write the Number Word

1. I have three children.

   I have one boy and __two__ girls.

2. I have four children.

   I have _____ girl and three boys.

3. I have five children.

   I have two boys and _____ girls.

4. I have six pets.

   I have one snake and _____ birds.

5. I have two pets.

   I have _____ pup and _____ bird.

6. Uncle Ted has ten pets.

   He has _____ pups and four snakes.

PRACTICE 3: Write *has* **or** *have*

1. I _have_ three children.

2. I _____ a pet shop.

3. Mr. Oliver _____ four children.

4. He _____ one girl and three boys.

5. Mr. and Mrs. Oliver _____ a pup.

6. Uncle Ted _____ a pet shop.

7. Mr. and Mrs. Hill _____ a boy and a girl.

8. I do not _____ children.

9. The woman _____ an apple.

10. Do you _____ children?

PRACTICE 4: Make Questions with *do*

1. You have children.

   Do you have children?

2. Mr. and Mrs. Oliver have four children.

   _____

3. Mr. and Mrs. Hill have three children.

   _____

4. Mr. and Mrs. Oliver have a pup.

   _____

5. The children have a box.

   _____

6. You have two girls.

   _____

7. Mr. and Mrs. Hill have one boy and two girls.

   _____

8. The children have a quarter.

   _____

PRACTICE 5: Answer the Questions with *Yes*

1. Do you have children?

   _____Yes, I do._____

2. Do Mr. and Mrs. Oliver have four children?

   _____

3. Do the Hills have two girls?

   _____

4. Do the children have a box?

   _____

5. Do the Hills have a tent?

   _____

6. Do the children have a quarter?

   _____

7. Do you have a pup?

   _____

8. Do you have a quarter?

   _____

PRACTICE 6: Answer the Questions with *No*

1. Do the Hills have five children?

   No, they don't.

2. Do you live in Indian Valley?

   _____

3. Do the Olivers have one boy?

   _____

4. Do you live on York Street?

   _____

5. Do the children have a snake?

   _____

6. Do Mr. and Mrs. Oliver have a bird?

   _____

7. Do you have four boys?

   _____

8. Do the boy and girl have a pet shop?

   _____

Note to the teacher: The word *don't* is new here.

PRACTICE 7: Make Questions with *Does*

1. Uncle Ted has a pet shop.

   Does Uncle Ted have a pet shop?

2. Uncle Ted has two snakes.

   _____

3. The man has an apple in his hand.

   _____

4. Mrs. Bird has one boy.

   _____

5. Mr. Oliver has a pup.

   _____

6. Mrs. Hill has three children.

   _____

7. The woman has a shop.

   _____

8. The girl has a snake.

   _____

Note to the teacher: The word *does* is new here.

PRACTICE 8: Answer the Questions with *Yes*

1. Does Uncle Ted have a pet shop?

   <u>Yes, he does.</u>

2. Does Mrs. Bird have one boy?

   _____

3. Does Mr. Oliver have a pup?

   _____

4. Does Uncle Ted have two snakes?

   _____

5. Does Mrs. Hill have three children?

   _____

6. Does the woman have a shop?

   _____

7. Does the girl have a pup?

   _____

8. Does the man have an apple in his hand?

   _____

PRACTICE 9: Answer the Questions with No

1. Does Mrs. Bird have a girl?

   <u>No, she doesn't.</u>

2. Does Uncle Ted live in Indian Valley?

   _____

3. Does the girl have a snake?

   _____

4. Does Mr. Oliver have one boy?

   _____

5. Does Mrs. Hill have five children?

   _____

6. Does the boy have a pet shop?

   _____

7. Does the woman live on York Street?

   _____

8. Does Ed have a pup?

   _____

Note to the teacher: The word *doesn't* is new here.

PRACTICE 10: Listen and Write

Listen to the teacher. Write the number words.

1. I have __three__ children.

2. I have _____ boy.

3. I have _____ girls.

4. Uncle Ted has _____ pups.

5. He has _____ snakes.

6. He has _____ birds.

7. I have _____ children.

Note to the teacher: Use only the number words for 1-6 and 10 in this practice.

PRACTICE 1: Make Questions

1. Mr. and Mrs. Hill have three children.

   <u>Do Mr. and Mrs. Hill have three children?</u>

2. The Olivers have four children.

   _____

3. Uncle Ted has a pet shop.

   _____

4. Cal is Mrs. Bird's boy.

   _____

5. Mrs. Bird has one boy.

   _____

6. The fish are in the pan.

   _____

7. The zipper is in the box.

   _____

8. Glenn and Liz are fishing in the river.

   _____

Note to the teacher: Have the students give short oral answers (*Yes, they do. No, they don't.*) to the questions they make.

PRACTICE 2: Write the Word with -'s

1. Mr. Oliver has a pup.

   This is _Mr. Oliver's_ pup.

2. Ted has a pan.

   This is _____ pan.

3. The children have a box.

   This is the _____ box.

4. The girl has a bird.

   This is the _____ bird.

5. Mrs. Hill has one box.

   This is _____ box.

6. Mr. Oliver has one girl.

   This is _____ girl.

7. Uncle Ted has a pet shop.

   This is _____ pet shop.

8. Ann has a dish.

   This is _____ dish.

PRACTICE 3: Write *in, on, at*

1. Mrs. Bird lives __in__ Indian Valley.

2. Mrs. Bird lives _____ 9 Valley Street.

3. The Olivers live _____ River Street.

4. They live _____ 426 River Street.

5. The pet shop is _____ York Street.

6. They are fishing _____ the river.

PRACTICE 4: Write *at, for, to, up*

1. The Hills are looking __at__ the fish.

2. He gives the fish _____ the children.

3. They thank him _____ the fish.

4. Cal picks _____ a box.

5. Dan gives a cup _____ Cal.

6. Uncle Ted picks _____ the snake.

7. Glenn Hill is looking _____ his girls.

8. The children thank the man _____ the pan.

PRACTICE 5: Write *her* **or** *him*

1. The children thank Uncle Ted.

   They thank __him__ .

2. Ed gives the apple to the woman.

   He gives the apple to _____ .

3. Ann sells the box to the man.

   She sells the box to _____ .

4. Queen runs to Mrs. Oliver.

   The pup runs to _____ .

5. The girls are looking at Bob.

   They are looking at _____ .

PRACTICE 6: Listen and Write

1. They have __a__ boy.

2. This is _____ egg.

3. Uncle Ted has _____ pet shop.

4. The children have _____ apple.

5. Mr. Oliver has _____ pup.

6. She puts _____ olive in the dish.

Note to the teacher: Use *a* and *an* in the blanks, but do not emphasize these words as you say the sentences. Do not pronounce *a* as /ay/.